How To Draw
404 Things
For Girls

How To Draw
404 Things
For Girls

Published by Top That! Publishing plc
Tide Mill Way, Woodbridge, Suffolk, IP12 IAP, UK
Copyright © 2012 Top That! Publishing plc
All rights reserved.
0 2 4 6 8 9 7 5 3 1
Printed and bound in China

fairy

Wizard

Minotaur

House Goblin

Ice Queen   # Yeti

Knight   Dwarf

Witch

Elf King

Phoenix

Gremlin

Mermaid

Dragon

Pixie   Zombie

Fairy Queen   # Tree Man

Leprechaun

Swamp ogre

Alien

Nymph

Pegasus

Flot Smudger

Two-headed Dog

Giant octopus

Grim Reaper

Prince Charming

Jack Frost   # Sorceress

fraggle Snap

flower fairy

Gnome

Big Bad Wolf

Snotter

Centaur

Thunder Bird

Three-headed ogre

Cave Troll

Dwarf Lady

Elf Queen

Barbarian

Unicorn

King Poseidon

Lesser-spotted Snotter

Giant Worm

Hobgoblin

Tree Lady

Sorcerer   Big foot

Wood Troll   # Bogeyman

corn fairy

cyclops

Mug Flump

Will'o'Wisp

Sphinx

Griffin

Lizard Man   Sea Troll

White Witch

Nessie

Fairy King   # Unifaun

Medusa

Princess

Harpie

Mushroom Man

Snicker Toad

Giant Spider

Warlock

Mountain Troll

Sandman

Wood Elf

Jabberwocky

Goat Sucker

Giant crab

Sprite

Spring-heeled Jack

Siren

Dwarf Lord

Wood Goblin

Gargoyle

Kraken

Hippogrif

Bogie

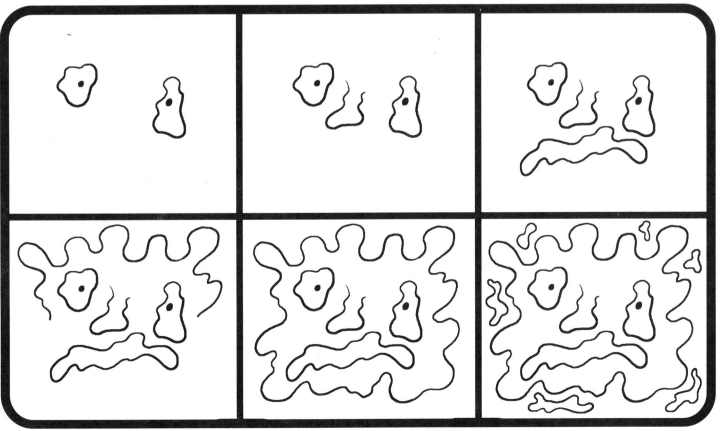

Jub Jub Bird

Cave Goblin

Limey Slop

Borogrove

Shape Changer

Water Nymph

Snarcrack

Earth Titan

Bander Snatch

Two-headed Snake

Galumph

Hades

Tum Tum

Slithy Tove

Fire Titan

Bottlenose dolphin

Moorish Idol

Dolphin Fish

Yellowfin Tuna

Rockhopper Penguin

Northern Right Whale

Seahorse

Dolphin and Calf

Great White Shark

Yellow Tang

Banded Pipefish

Puffer Fish

Shrimp

Dugong

Brown Pelican

Lantern fish

Squid

Laughing Dolphin

Parrot fish

Chinstrap Penguin

Lionfish

Bonnethead Shark

Common Dolphin

Cod

Elephant Fish

Sperm Whale

Dolphins playing

Blue Marlin

common Puffin

Lobster

clownfish

Hammerhead Shark

Permit Fish

Spotted Dolphin

cuttlefish

Pilot whale

Skate

Hermit crab

Blue Whale

Fire Goby

Walrus

Humpback Dolphin

Black Dragonfish

Basking Shark

Queen Angelfish

Nautilus

Seagull

Dolphin with ball

Blue Tang

Mandarin fish

Picasso Triggerfish

Red Snapper

Emperor Penguin with egg

octopus

Dolphin jumping

Manta Ray

Narwhal

Spider crab

Sea Lion

Soldier Fish

Chromis fish

Stingray

four-Eyed Butterfly fish

Baby Seal

Dusky Dolphin

Moonfish

Anglerfish

Marine Iguana

Humpback Whale

Flying Fish

Elephant Seal

Commerson's Dolphin

Butterfly fish

oarfish

Manatee

Sea Turtle

Killer Whale (orca)

Unicorn Fish

Sailfish

Lumpsucker

Baby Dolphin

Pineapple fish

Spotted oreo

Softshell Turtle

Swordfish

Jellyfish

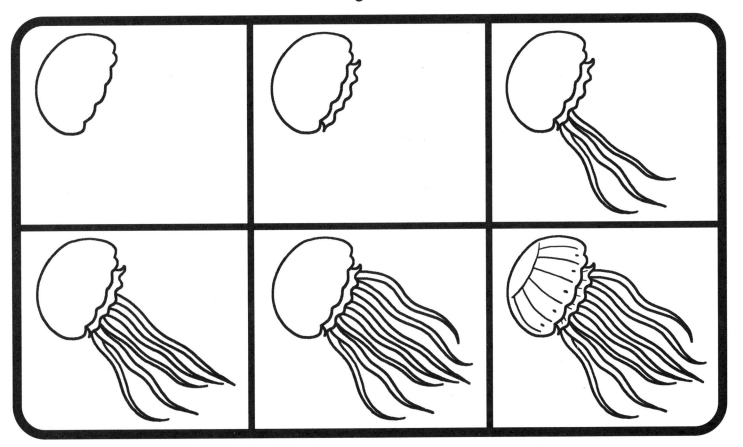

Seal

Blue-Footed Booby

Starfish

Toadfish

cockatoo fish

Smiling Dolphin

Sea Slug

Sea otter

Horseshoe crab

Clown Knife Fish

Moon Jellyfish

Big-Eye Thresher Shark

Brittle Star

Tail-Walking Dolphin

Moray Eel

Woodland Fairy

Tooth Fairy

Water Fairy

Fairy Godmother

Starbright

Toadstool fairy

corn Fairy

Fairy Queen

Flower Fairy

Moonbeam

christmas fairy

Buttercup

Flutter

Seaspray

Rainbow Fairy   Sunshine Fairy

Puddle

Whoosh

Glitter

Trixie

Velvet

Snoozy

Ruby   Daisy

Blink

Sparkle

Bubbles

Firefly

Emerald

Dewdrop

Dimples

Fluffy

Blush

Freckles

Rose

Snowdrop

Beauty

Loveheart

Twizzle

Sapphire

Dazzle   # Misty

Dizzy

Lollipop

candy

fizz

Goldie

Charm

Snowflake   Jester

Whistler

Smudge

crystal

Tiny

Sunflower

Fidget

chuckles   cuddles

Lotus

Bumble

Shuffle   # Jasmine

Raven

Alpine

Blossom   # Ariel

Snuggles

Minty

Tulip

Amble

cupcake

Seashell

Prancer   Willow

flash

flora

Hazel

Pebble

frazzle

Hawkwind

Pinky   # Butterscotch

Venus

Jacaranda

Nibs

Cherry

Violet

Grace

Nixie

Coral

Andromeda

Petunia

Dragonfly

Baubles

Nightingale

Indigo

Elfin

Jiggle

Melody

Arab

Thoroughbred

Friesian

Dartmoor

Lusitano

Lipizzaner

Mustang

Piebald

Shire

Falabella

Appaloosa

Shetland Pony

Palomino

Norwegian Fjord pony

Breton

Pinto

Walking

Trotting

Cantering

Galloping

Jumping

Eating grass

Rearing

Tethered

circus horse

Whinnying

Prehistoric horse

Horse and rosette

Dressage horse

Bridled horse

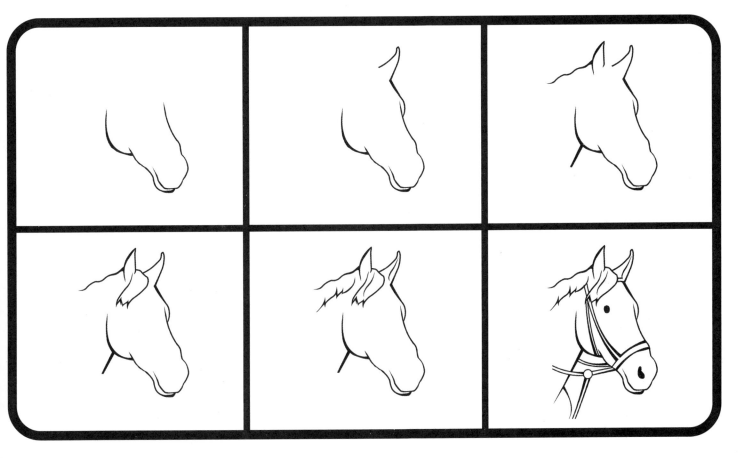

Bucking bronco with rider

Polo pony with rider

Mother and foal

Racehorse with blinkers

Medieval tournament horse

Expression; ears forward

Expression; ears back

Harness racing

classical equitation

Eventing horse

Two heads nuzzling

Show horse

fantasy horse - unicorn head

fantasy horse - pegasus full body

fantasy horse - pegasus head

fantasy horse - unicorn full body

Mustang Close-up

Thoroughbred Close-up

Piebald pony

Eating hay

Plaited tail

Plaited mane

Horse in horsebox

Rear view of saddle

Horse lying down

Horse rolling over

Horse pawing the ground

Horse with blanket

foal

Horse being re-shod

Horse led with halter

Police horse

Jockey on horse

Canadian Mountie horse

Horse drinking

Horse guards

Horse with Western saddle

Horses with nose markings

Show jumping

foal suckling mother

Play fighting

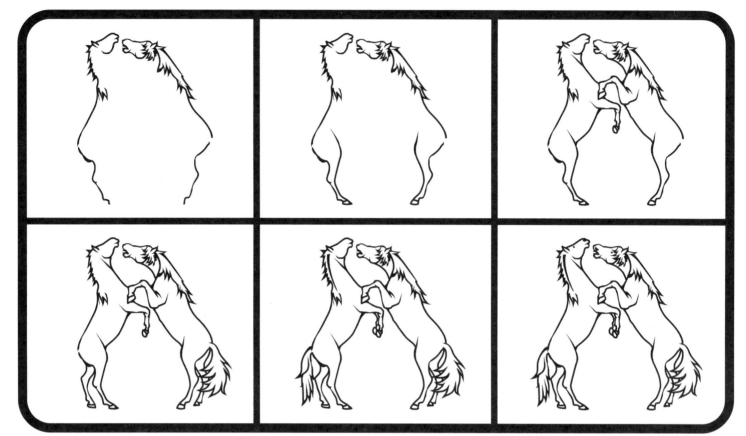

Horse jumping a countryside fence

Horse trotting with rider

Buck-toothed cartoon horse

cartoon pony

cartoon seahorse

cartoon pegasus

cartoon horse - galloping

Cool horse

Cool pony

cartoon foal - cantering

cartoon old horse

Pop star pony

cartoon horse – flower in mouth

Horse over stable door

Horse - rear view

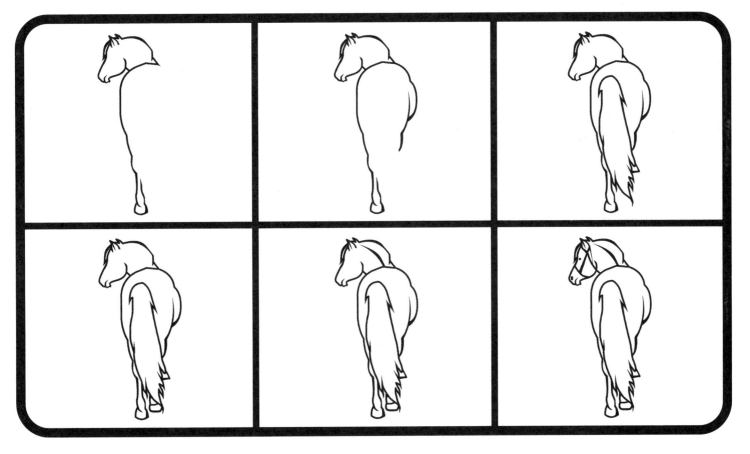

Jockey

Bucking horse

Horse cantering through water

Horse high-trotting

Cowboy

Horse Chewing

Petting

Horse and cart

Horses fighting

Wild horse

Miniature

Horse with Native American